THIS BEN 10 ALIEN FORCE™ ANNUAL BELONGS TO

Adam Mellis

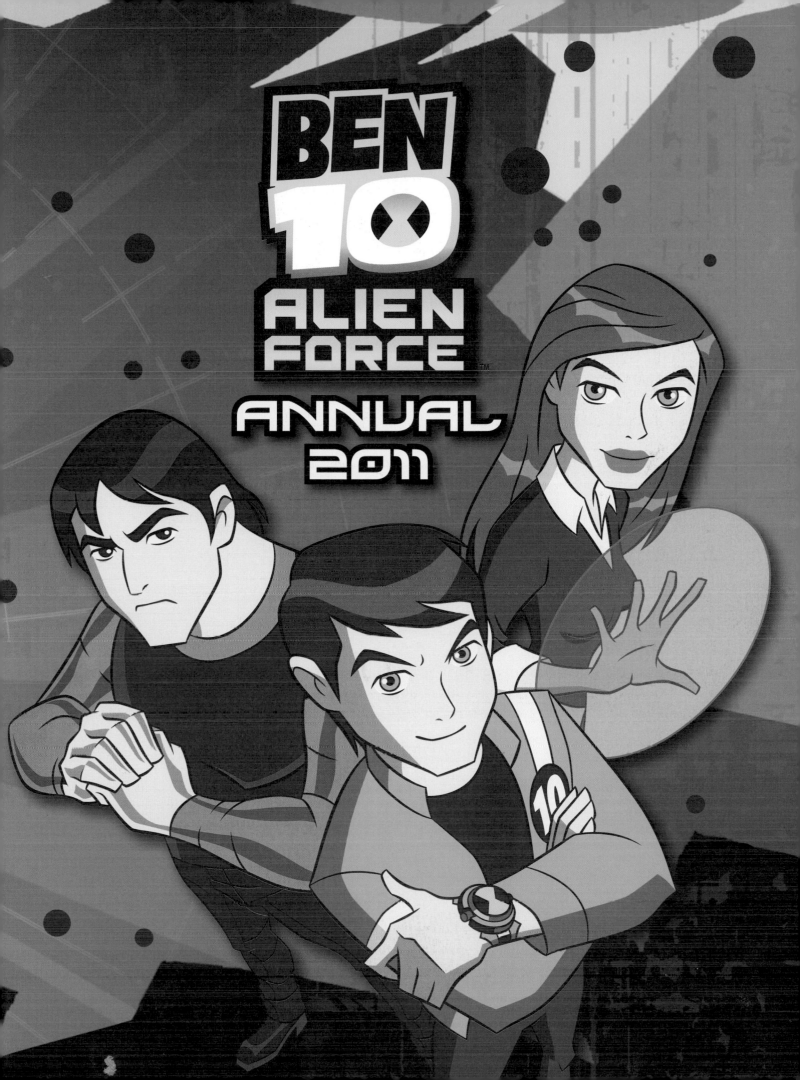

CONTENTS

EGMONT

We bring stories to life

First published in Great Britain 2010 by Egmont UK Limited
239 Kensington High Street, London W8 6SA
Text by Laura Milne, Design by Candice Bekir

Cartoon Network, the logo, BEN 10 ALIEN FORCE and all related
characters and elements are trademarks of and © 2010 Cartoon Network.
All rights reserved

ISBN 978 1 4052 5252 2
1 3 5 7 9 10 8 6 4 2
Printed in Italy

BEN 10 RETURNS

After keeping the Omnitrix hidden and unused for the past five years, Ben is now back, turning alien once again!

When he discovers that his Grandpa Max has gone missing, and has his first encounter with a scary DNAlien, Ben knows it's time to go hero. So he activates the Omnitrix again – only to find that it has re-programmed itself and has a brand new set of ten awesome alien heroes to get to grips with!

The bonus is that Ben has the help of his cousin Gwen who has magical superpowers of her own, and former enemy Kevin E. Levin has joined forces with them, to lend some serious muscle.

Now you can join the team! Get the low-down on the good guys and arm yourself with info on the bad guys. Turn to the puzzles and quizzes to get your grey cells working, and check out the stories to find out what Ben and his friends get up to.

FIND GRANDPA MAX!

If you look closely, you'll find 10 hidden pictures of Grandpa Max like this one throughout the book. Can you find them all?

Answers on pages 68 and 69.

WHAT ARE YOU WAITING FOR? LET'S KICK ALIEN BUTT!

BEN TENNYSON

Ben is a fun and loyal 15 year-old. When he realises his Grandpa Max has gone missing, Ben knows it's time to turn to the Omnitrix once again.

"TIME TO GO HERO AGAIN!"

STRENGTHS

• Ben is brave and he doesn't hesitate to help when any friend or family member is in trouble.

• Ben is trustworthy and adopts the role of leader now that Max has gone AWOL.

WEAKNESSES

• Sometimes Ben needs to have more confidence in himself — he is the ultimate superhero, after all!

• Ben can rush headlong into things — but he's learning to think ahead more.

THE OMNITRIX

The Omnitrix is a watch-like device from outer space, and it allows Ben to turn into different aliens. Unfortunately the Omnitrix doesn't come with an instruction manual – it's all down to Ben to work it out!

GWEN TENNYSON

Gwen is Ben's 15 year-old cousin. She is gutsy, dependable and determined to help Ben on his adventures.

"I WILL SEE WHAT I CAN DO"

ALIEN GENES

Gwen learns more about her magic powers all the time. She discovers that humans with alien ancestors are pretty common, and that she would have inherited her powers from Grandpa Max.

STRENGTHS

• Gwen has her own superpowers, and she can form magical orbs, lasers and platforms.

• Gwen is a force to be reckoned with, and she is also sensible and level-headed.

WEAKNESSES

• Sometimes Gwen can be too proud and stubborn for her own good — these traits can get her into trouble.

• Gwen does give good advice — but sometimes she can seem a bit of a know-it-all!

KEVIN E. LEVIN

After dealing in illegal alien technology and spending time in the Null Void (an extra-dimensional prison), 16-year-old Kevin has now turned his back on crime and has joined forces with Ben and Gwen in the fight against evil.

"TAKE YOUR BEST SHOT"

STRENGTHS

• Kevin has the power to absorb any solid material, such as wood, metal, steel and concrete — making him capable of lending some serious muscle!

• He is very knowledgeable about the bad guys and their alien technology.

WEAKNESSES

• Although he is now mostly a reformed character, Kevin can still sometimes be tempted to steal goods and equipment from the villains.

• Kevin can be headstrong and stubborn.

KEVIN'S CAR

Kevin provides the wheels for the team and drives this cool green sports car from the 1970s. It's the ultimate action cruiser, filled with hidden alien technology and battle capabilities.

MAX TENNYSON

Max is Ben and Gwen's Grandpa. He is a retired member of the Plumbers, an intergalactic police force that fights evil villains to help save the world. At the beginning of Alien Force, Max has mysteriously gone missing.

"YOU'RE A SIGHT FOR SORE EYES"

STRENGTHS

• Max is kind, loyal, good fun and he's really proud of his grandkids.

• As a former Plumber, Max is tough and brave and equipped with the know-how to defeat evil villains.

WEAKNESSES

• Sometimes Max seems to know more than he's letting on, but really he's just protecting his grandkids.

• The villains are always out to get their revenge on Max.

SWAMPFIRE

Swampfire is a plant-like alien and is Ben's first alien transformation in five years. He's like a living swamp who can produce highly flammable – and highly stinky – methane gas. Swampfire is extremely strong and has a regenerative ability that allows him to tunnel underground in vine form and root himself into the ground.

GOOD GUY

SWAMPFIRE
FACT FILE

AS HE IS MADE OF MUD, HE IS JUST ABOUT SAFE FROM ALL PHYSICAL HARM, AS THINGS GO RIGHT THROUGH HIM!

HE CAN SHOOT FLAMES FROM HIS HANDS LIKE A FLAMETHROWER.

HE IS ABLE TO REGENERATE SEVERED LIMBS – HIS OWN, AND ANYONE ELSE'S.

TANGLED ROOTS

Swampfire has thrown out some vine roots to trap a nasty villain. Follow the trails to work out which one leads to the bad guy. Then, can you identify the baddy from his shadow? Write his name on the dotted line.

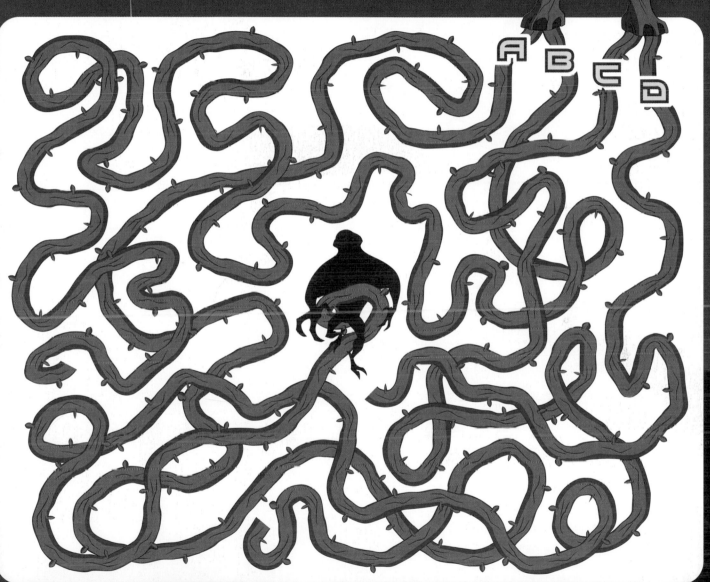

The bad guy is a   d n a l i e n

CHROMASTONE

ChromaStone is a real tough guy! He is a living crystal, his body made up of almost indestructible silicone. He can absorb energy (like a conductor) and channel it into laser blasts. ChromaStone has superhuman strength and there is almost nothing that can harm him.

GOOD GUY

CHROMASTONE FACT FILE

HAS SHARDS OF TOUGH CRYSTAL ATTACHED TO HIS HEAD, CHEST AND BACK.

LASER BEAMS BLASTED AT HIM BY ALIEN WEAPONS BOUNCE STRAIGHT OFF HIS BODY.

CAN ABSORB RADIATION AND TRANSFORM IT INTO ANY KIND OF LIGHT (INCLUDING LASERS).

LASER BLASTER

ChromaStone is aiming laser blasts at a HighBreed! Look at the ways in which the lasers reflect and bounce off the shields. Can you work out which number ChromaStone will be successful in bringing down the bad guy?

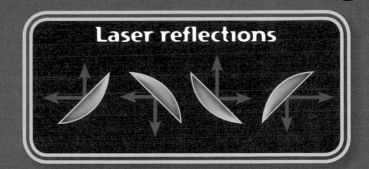

Laser reflections

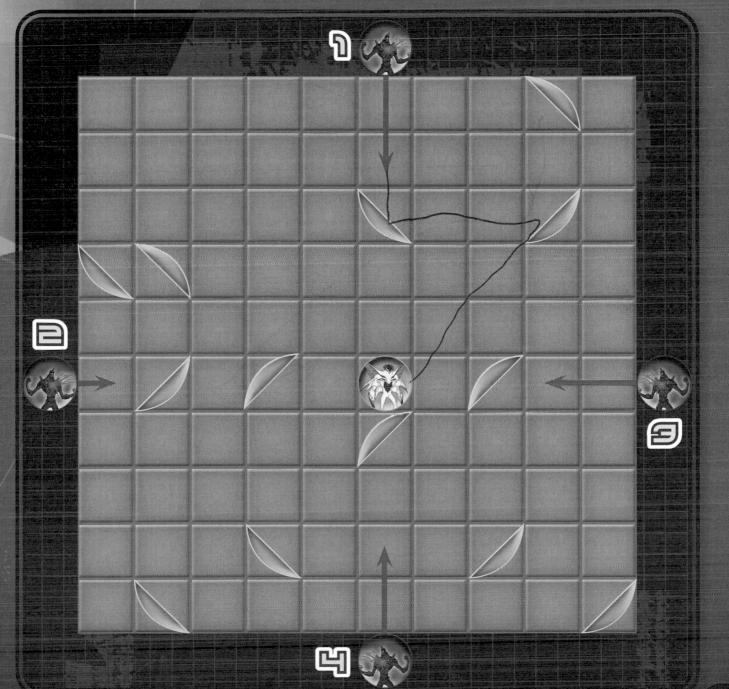

SATURDAYS ARE MY FAVORITE DAY. YOU CAN SLEEP IN.

YOU CAN WEAR WHATEVER YOU WANT.

YOU CAN EAT BREAKFAST FOR LUNCH. IT'S THE PERFECT *LAZY DAY*.

DON'T FORGET YOUR CHORES!

BUT IT'S MY LAZY DAY!

BEN, YOU KNOW WE DON'T CONDONE LAZINESS.

WELL, I SUPPOSE YOUR CHORES CAN WAIT.

ENJOY YOUR "LAZY DAY"!

WHERE ARE WE HEADED?

TO THE WIND FARM OUTSIDE OF TOWN.

HOW DO YOU FARM WIND? YOU MUST NEED A REALLY BIG TRACTOR!

MAYBE HE'S PULLING YOU OVER FOR DRIVING UNDER THE INFLUENCE OF A LAME SENSE OF HUMOR.

WOOO WOOO WOOO

CRUD.

IS THERE A PROBLEM, OFFICER?

DO YOU HAVE ANY IDEA HOW FAST YOU WERE DRIVING?!

THE SPEED LIMIT?

YOU WERE GOING TWENTY MILES PER HOUR UNDER THE SPEED LIMIT!

HUH?

NO SENSE RUSHING ANYWHERE TODAY. I'LL LET YOU GO WITH A WARNING.

THANKS!

I CAN'T BELIEVE YOU ALMOST GOT A TICKET FOR BEING TOO SLOW.

THAT DOESN'T LEAVE THIS CAR. I'M NEVER SLOW.

EVERYONE'S ACTING A LITTLE WEIRD TODAY.

I BET THEY'VE GOT SOMETHING TO DO WITH IT.

GAS.

NOT ME!

NO, THERE! THAT MUST BE WHAT'S MAKING EVERYONE SO APATHETIC!

KEEP IT FLOWING! THEY WON'T BE ABLE TO STOP US!

MAYBE I SHOULDN'T BOTHER...

THE OMNITRIX, YOU HAVE TO...

NEED SOMEONE WHOSE ALWAYS CHILLIN'...

THERE'S STILL A FEW HOURS LEFT TO DO NOTHING.

YOU DIDN'T FORGET THIS, DID YOU?

BEN'S CHORES
☐ CLEAN ROOM
☐ TAKE OUT TRASH
☐ DISHES
☐ VACUUM
☐ CLEAN GARAGE
☐ LAUNDRY

BUT IT'S MY LAZY DAY!

YOU HAD ALL DAY TO BE LAZY. NOW GET TO WORK.

THIS IS THE WORST LAZY DAY EVER.

THE END

Ben, Gwen, Kevin and Grandpa Max come up against three main groups of villains in Alien Force – the HighBreed, DNAliens and the Forever Knights.

THE HIGHBREED

The HighBreed are power crazy. They are an alien race from the planet Darama, and they are Ben and the gang's most dangerous enemy. They think of themselves as the highest life-form in the universe and believe that they were the very first race ever to exist.

HIGHBREED ID

- Tall, humanoid beings with fold-out wings on their back.

- Hugely powerful — can overpower aliens larger than themselves.

- Can fire their fingertips like darts.

The HighBreed are determined to cleanse the universe of all races except themselves – and Earth is their next target! They think that coming into contact with other races will contaminate them, and they have DNAliens to do their dirty work for them.

DNALiENS

DNAliens are hybrids of humans and aliens, and they are servants of the HighBreed. They are sneaky, and are able to disguise themselves as humans using special identity masks.

DNAliens are created by attaching a facehugger-like parasite called a Xenocyte to a human host.

DNALIEN ID

- Pale brown skin with vicious tentacles in their chest.

- Fairly strong and are able to spit out a horrible sticky slime.

- They prefer cold climates and build weather control centres.

FOREVER KNIGHTS

The Forever Knights are a secret society first formed during the Middle Ages – with the purpose of slaying a dragon. They now trade in illegal alien technology, using it for their own personal power.

FOREVER KNIGHTS ID

- Like true knights, they wear a complete suit of body armour.

- They use powerful laser lances as weapons.

- They trade with the HighBreed, and use DNAliens as go-betweens.

JET RAY

Whenever Ben needs speed, he turns into Jet Ray! Jet Ray is a manta-ray-like alien capable of flying and swimming faster than the speed of sound. He can attack an enemy by firing vicious neuroshock blasts from his eyes and tail.

GOOD GUY

JET RAY FACT FILE

HIS HOME PLANET (AEROPELA) IS COMPLETELY COVERED IN WATER – WHICH IS WHY HE HAS DEVELOPED TO EITHER FLY OR SWIM.

HE CAN MANOEUVRE EASILY AS HE FLIES AT TOP SPEEDS, HELPING HIM DODGE ATTACKS.

HE HAS WEBBED ARMS AND POISONOUS STINGERS ON HIS HEAD.

SPEEDY MISSION

Some Forever Knights are chasing Gwen. Can you show Jet Ray the quickest flying route to save her? The quickest route is the one with the smallest total when the numbers are added together. Use the spaces at the bottom to fill in the totals for each route.

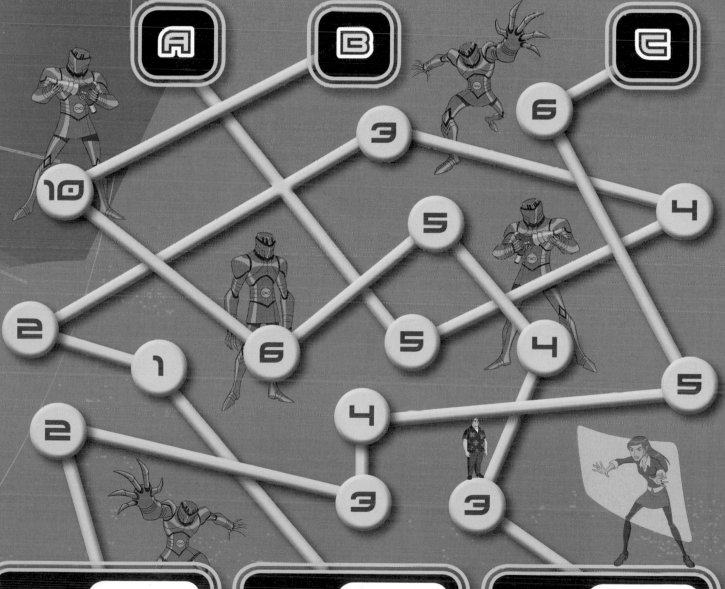

Total =

Total =

Total =

HUMUNGOUSAUR

Humungousaur is Ben's largest and most powerful alien form. He's a huge dinosaur alien, and is able to increase his body size and weight whenever the job calls for it!

GOOD GUY

1

HUMUNGOUSAUR FACT FILE

HUMUNGOUSAUR'S THICK LAYER OF SKIN PROTECTS HIM FROM MOST ATTACKS.

HE CAN GROW TO AN AMAZING 18 METRES IN HEIGHT.

WHEN HE GROWS, HE DEVELOPS DINOSAUR-LIKE SPIKES ON HIS HEAD, BACK AND TAIL.

ULTIMATE POWER

 Humungousaur is about to do battle with a HighBreed, so he decides it's time to put on some weight! Pictures 1 and 2 look the same but there are 5 differences in picture 2. Can you spot them all?

The hulking Humungousaur has his hands full, holding up a collapsing bridge. How do you think it turns out? In the box, write or draw what you think happens next.

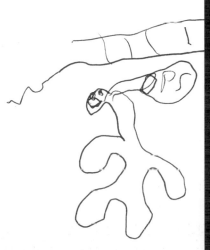

SPIDERMONKEY

His name says it all! A cross between a spider and a monkey, Spidermonkey is Ben's most agile alien. He can spin awesome giant spiderwebs and stick to walls – skills that prove really useful when trapping the bad guys.

GOOD GUY

SPIDERMONKEY FACT FILE

A NIMBLE MONKEY-LIKE ALIEN, WITH SIX LIMBS.

HIS SPIDERWEBS ARE MADE OF SILK AS HARD AS STEEL CABLE.

A CHATTERING, MISCHIEVOUS ALIEN WHO SOMETIMES SCREECHES LIKE A MONKEY.

WEB SEARCH

Spidermonkey has spun a strong web to trap some bad guys, but some good guys have got caught in there, too! Look for all these names in the grid. They can read up, down, across, backwards and diagonally.

THE BAD GUYS:
HIGHBREED
DNALIEN
FOREVER KNIGHT
VULKANUS
MORNINGSTAR
TECHADON
SEVEN SEVEN
DRAVEK

THE GOOD GUYS:
GRANDPA MAX
GWEN
KEVIN

```
A M B X A M A P D N A R G
F O R E V E R K N I G H T
C R D E G T E C H A D O N
H N M T R O N I I X D J L
K I G S E V E N S E V E N
D N A L I E N M E N B C T
D G V E A A T R L D M K L
C S T O M N B T S R U E W
G T H J O H T L M A J V F
C A R T G T R A T V S I T
X R V I G G W E N E T N S
T G H C B N E J G K F T N
D B A V U L K A N U S U O
```

When you've found all the names, unravel 8 unused letters from the middle of row 4 in the grid to spell out a very special object.

The hidden object is:

_o m n a t r i x_

SHIP SHAPE

WRITER • CHARLOTTE FULLERTON   ART & COVER • MIN S. KU
LETTERER • TRAVIS LANHAM   COLORIST • HEROIC AGE
EDITORS • ELISABETH V. GEHRLEIN & SEAN RYAN
BEN 10 CREATED BY MAN OF ACTION

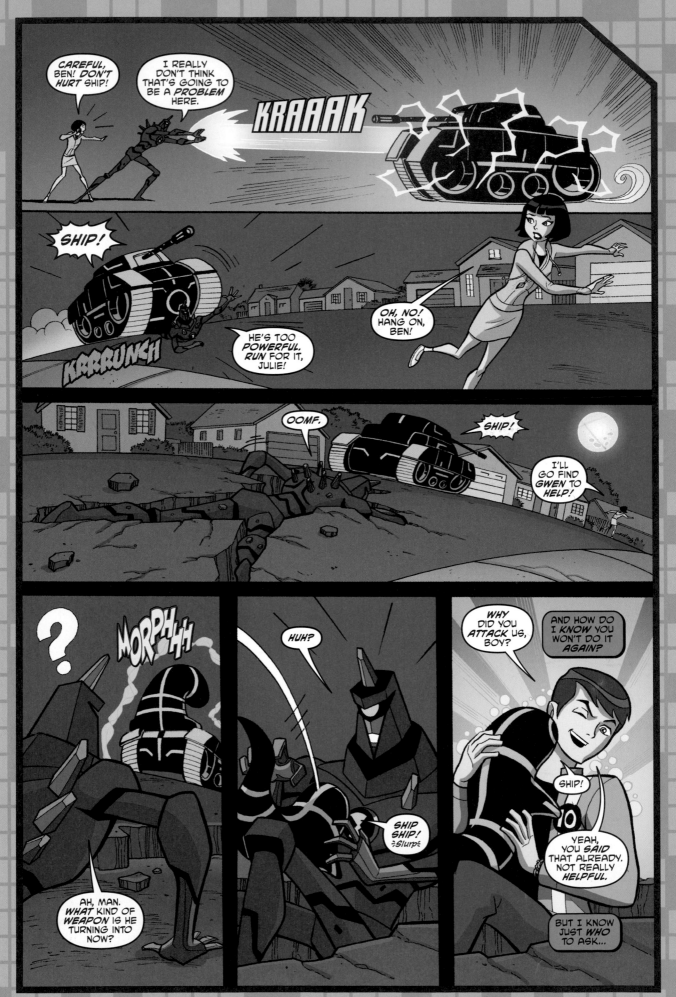

38

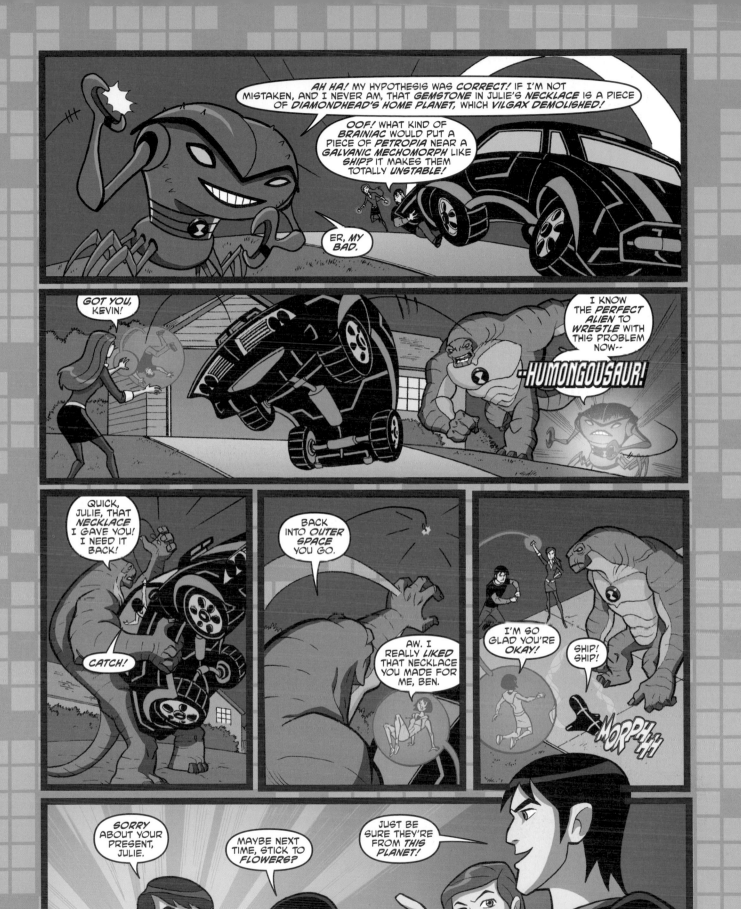

GOOP

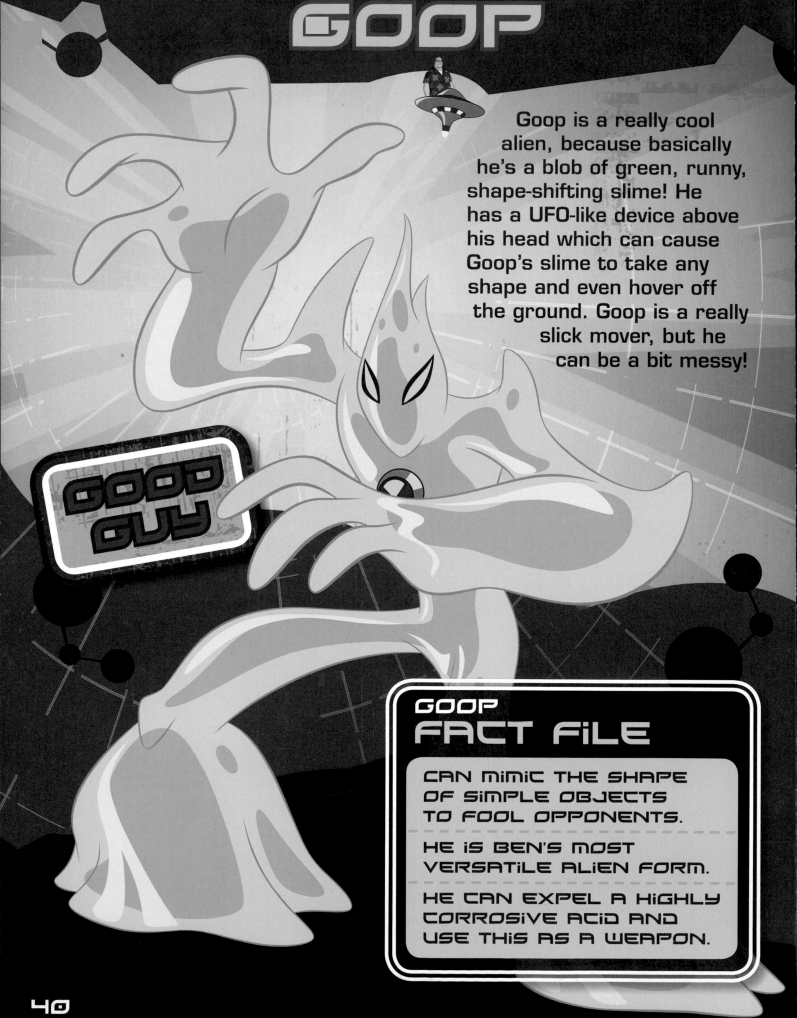

Goop is a really cool alien, because basically he's a blob of green, runny, shape-shifting slime! He has a UFO-like device above his head which can cause Goop's slime to take any shape and even hover off the ground. Goop is a really slick mover, but he can be a bit messy!

GOOD GUY

GOOP FACT FILE

CAN MIMIC THE SHAPE OF SIMPLE OBJECTS TO FOOL OPPONENTS.

HE IS BEN'S MOST VERSATILE ALIEN FORM.

HE CAN EXPEL A HIGHLY CORROSIVE ACID AND USE THIS AS A WEAPON.

Goop is a master of disguise. Only two of these pictures of the shape-shifting alien are identical – can you spot them?

A

B

C

D

E

F

Goop has the amazing power to turn into the shape of any simple object. What would you turn into, if you were Goop? Perhaps a phone, a boat or a carton of milkshake? Draw your design here.

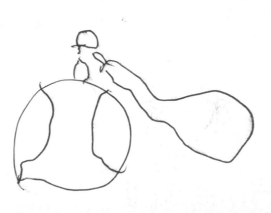

With his crab-like body, Brain Storm looks like a seafood platter! But appearances can be deceptive, and Brain Storm is a genius – Ben's most intelligent alien. He is also physically powerful, with sharp pincers and a tough exoskeleton.

BRAIN STORM FACT FILE

CAN OPEN HIS SHELL TO REVEAL HIS HUGE BRAIN.

HE CAN CONTROL ELECTRICAL ENERGY JUST BY THINKING HARD ENOUGH.

WITH ENOUGH CONCENTRATION, BRAIN STORM CAN EVEN LEVITATE IN THE AIR!

GOOD GUY

CRYPTIC CODE

Brain Storm has intercepted a message from the HighBreed to the DNAliens. Can you work it out? Start from the top row (go from left to right), and write every 3rd letter in the space at the bottom.

AJTKUHLMEDDSVEE AL

CMMREGEATACDTABVJLRNPEKJS

ETMFLUDFSJIT KNNQSORWT

UVBXTECDABGT ATVCDS

the crturs must not beat us

BIG CHILL

As a flying ghost, Big Chill is pretty creepy! He looks a bit like a blue moth, and when he folds up his wings and antennae, he has a spooky hooded appearance. He is incredibly strong but his main weapon is his chilly breath that can freeze anything solid.

GOOD GUY

BIG CHILL FACT FILE

HE'S A GHOST WHO CAN PASS THROUGH ANYTHING.

BIG CHILL CAN MAKE HIMSELF INVISIBLE.

HE CAN DROP THE TEMPERATURE OF ANYTHING TO FREEZING POINT.

NOW YOU SEE HIM . . .

Big Chill is turning invisible – can you help put him back together again? Find out which pieces are missing from Big Chill, and draw lines to match them up.

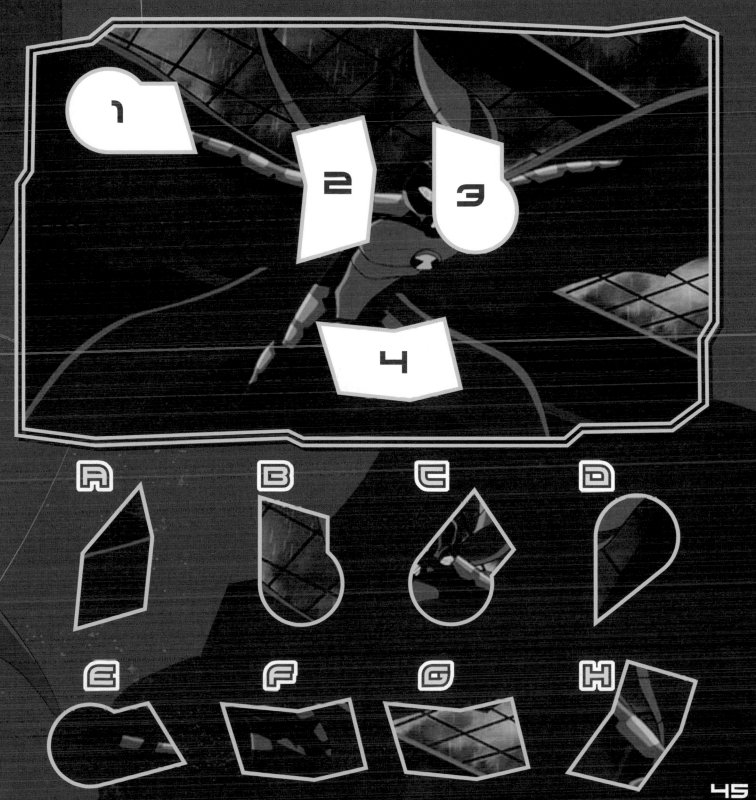

writer: CHARLOTTE FULLERTON
art and cover: MIN S. KU
letterer: SAL CIPRIANO
colorist: HI-FI
associate editor: SEAN RYAN
editor: ELISABETH V. GEHRLEIN
BEN 10 created by MAN OF ACTION

49

Echo Echo might be small and compact, but he's big in power. A living amplifier, Echo Echo can scream at high-pitched ultrasonic frequencies – enough to shatter steel, overload machinery and stop missiles in mid-flight.

GOOD GUY

ECHO ECHO
FACT FILE

HE HAS AN EAR-PIERCING, ULTRASONIC SCREAM.

ECHO ECHO CAN CHANNEL VIBRATIONS, AMPLIFY SOUNDS AND USE ECHOLOCATION.

HE CAN MAKE AS MANY COPIES OF HIMSELF AS HE LIKES – HANDY FOR CONFUSING THE BAD GUYS!

ECHO DRAW

Echo Echo has duplicated himself, but one of his clones has got muddled up. Use the coordinates to put him back together, by drawing the missing pieces into the second grid.

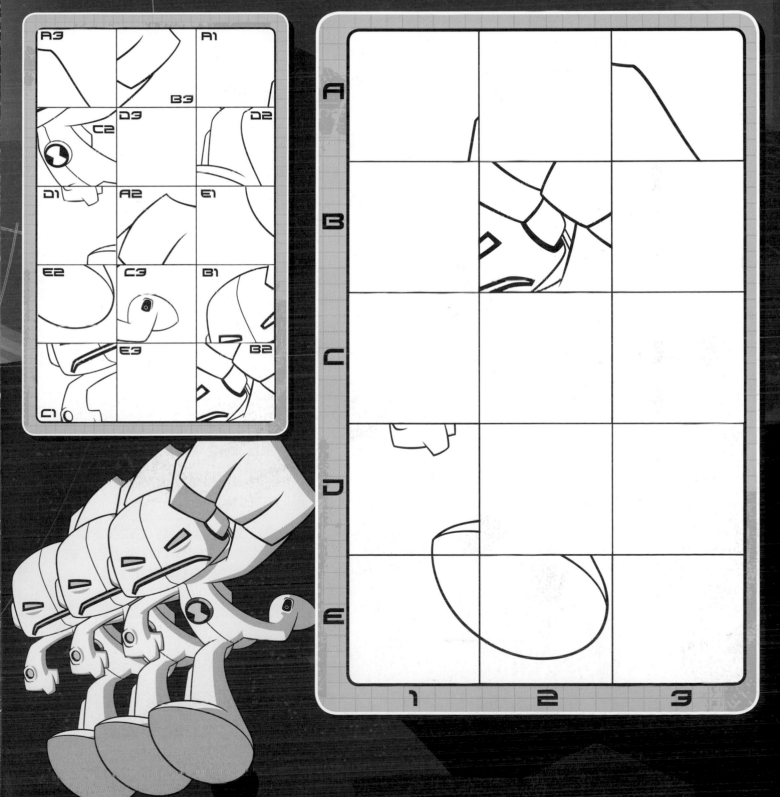

ALIEN X

Alien X is Ben's most powerful form and also the most mysterious and dangerous. Alien X has three distinct personalities – Serena (the voice of love), Bellicus (the voice of rage) and Ben (the voice of reason).

GOOD GUY

ALIEN X FACT FILE

TWO OF ALIEN X'S PERSONALITIES MUST BE IN AGREEMENT FOR HIM TO BE ABLE TO DO ANYTHING.

HE CAN WARP REALITY.

ALIEN X IS BEN'S LEAST FAVOURITE ALIEN FORM.

ALIEN X'S GRID

Alien X can be a tricky dude to handle. But can you handle this word grid? See if you can fit the words in the grid below. One has been done for you.

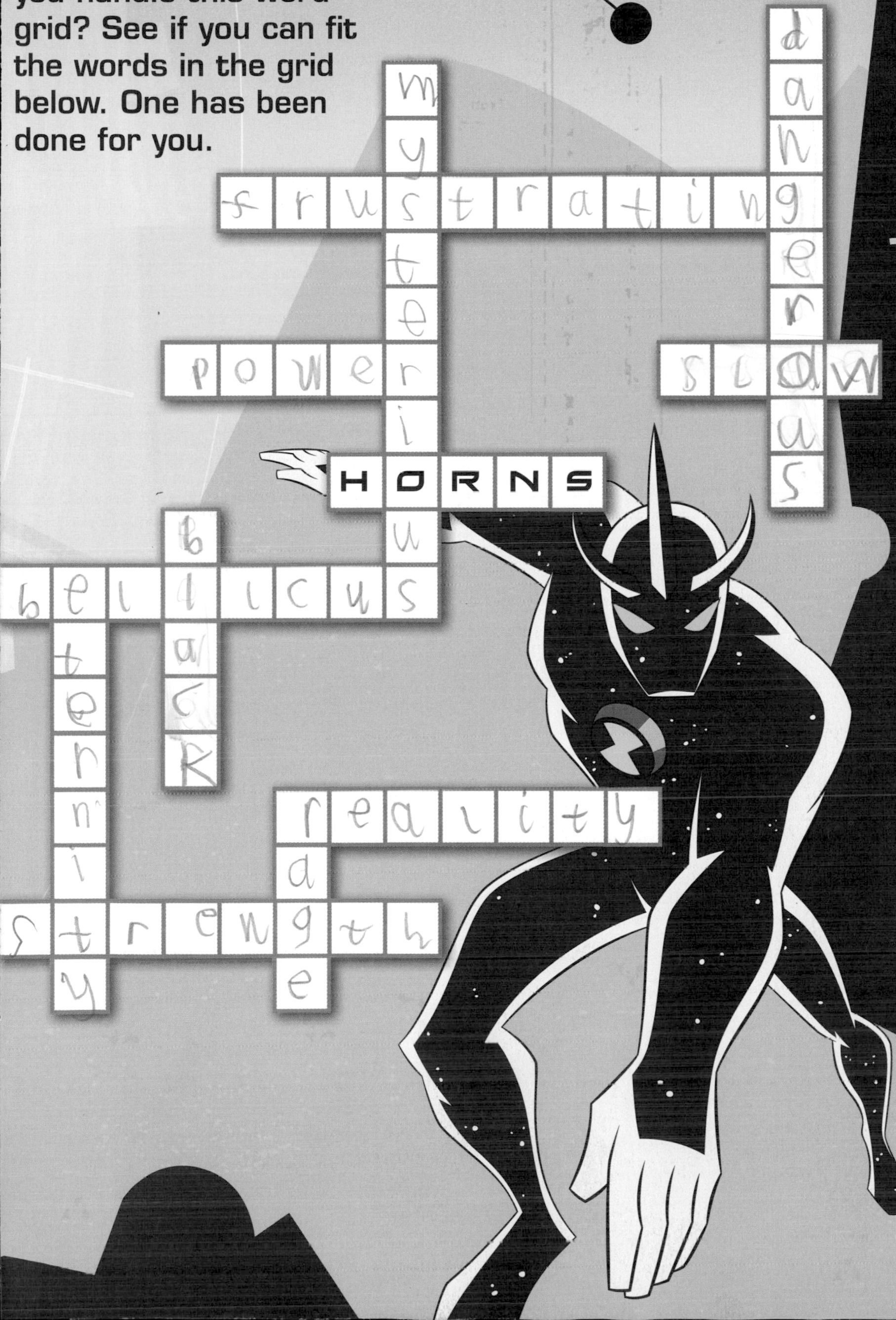

Grid answers:
- mysterious
- frustrating
- dangerous
- power
- slow
- HORNS
- bellicus
- black
- eternity
- reality
- rage
- strength

THAT'S NOT GOOD...

BRILLIANT! YOU *ACTIVATED* THE THING *AND* KNOCKED THE ONLY ONE WITH THE ANSWERS *UNCONSCIOUS!*

I DIDN'T SEE *YOU* STEPPING UP WITH A *MASTER PLAN!*

59... 58... 57...

EASY, BOYS. THE RISING TESTOSTERONE LEVELS CAN'T BE HELPING--AND, BESIDES, I'VE GOT AN *IDEA...*

LET ME SEE IF I CAN *TRANSLATE* THESE--OH-BOY...WELL, IT'S A *BOMB.*

OH, *WONDERFUL*... NICE OF THEM TO MAKE IT COUNT DOWN IN *ENGLISH...*

IT WAS PLANTED HERE MANY YEARS AGO BY *THE HIGHBREED* WHEN THEY FIRST DEVISED THEIR PLAN TO "CLEANSE" THE EARTH OF ITS "FILTHY RACES". OH, NICE...

IT'S SORT OF A *DOOMSDAY/FINAL-SOLUTION DEVICE* MEANT TO *DESTROY THE PLANET* IF THINGS DON'T GO THEIR WAY.

OKAY, HERE'S THE DEAL. IT'S *HIGHLY ILLEGAL*, SO I'VE NEVER MENTIONED IT BEFORE.

I *KNOW* HOW YOU FEEL ABOUT MY...*COLORFUL PAST.*

IT'S A PIECE OF *"LEVEL 10" TECH* THAT SHOULDN'T EVEN BE IN THIS *ARM OF THE GALAXY,* LET ALONE *EARTH.*

IT'S A *"TEMPORAL BOOMERANG"* THAT'LL ALLOW US TO TAKE ONE FIVE-MINUTE ROUND TRIP... *BACK IN TIME.*

PERFECT! WE CAN JUST GO BACK A COUPLE MINUTES AND STOP OURSELVES FROM ARMING THE THING!

DO I HAVE TO EXPLAIN *TIME PARADOXES* TO YOU? WE NEED TO GO BACK TO WHEN YOU KNOW WHO HAD THE KEY AND GET IT.

LOOK, JUST *PICK A TIME*--THINK OF *WHEN* YOU WANT TO GO--

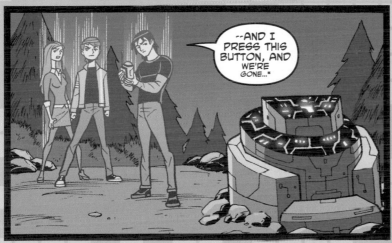

--AND I PRESS THIS BUTTON, AND WE'RE GONE...*

6...
5...
4...

WEIRD... I ACTUALLY *REMEMBER* HAVING THIS FIGHT WITH SOME *CREEPY BLUE ALIEN* THAT I THOUGHT WAS AFTER MY *CARD COLLECTION!*

I ALWAYS *THOUGHT* MY *BIG CHILL* FORM SEEMED *VAGUELY FAMILIAR*--NOW I KNOW *WHY!*

GOT IT!

WELL, *GOOD*-- SINCE OUR *FIVE MINUTES* ARE UP!

BEN, HURRY!

I HOPE THIS--

BIP BIP BIP

LET'S *BLOW* THIS TIME PERIOD...

4...
3...
2...

TOO CLOSE, MAN!

WHEW! WELL, *THAT* WAS AN *EXPERIENCE!* AND DEFINITELY *WEIRD* SEEING OURSELVES BACK THEN.

AND SINCE I DON'T REMEMBER HAVING EVER *MET* MY *15-YEAR-OLD SELF* FROM THE FUTURE--

--I BETTER *DISGUISE* MYSELF JUST TO BE SAFE. *BIG CHILL!*

NOW YOU'RE GETTING THE IDEA. BUT WE *STILL* NEED TO MAKE SURE WE DON'T RUN INTO *OUR* YOUNGER SELVES.

NO SWEAT.

YEAH, RIGHT...

I WAS *CUTE*, HUH...?

HEH. WELL...

I'LL SHOW YOU SKILLS. MAYBE THERE'S SOMETHING IN HERE TO MAKE YOU SMELL *BETTER*...

THERE SHE GOES, WITH HER UGLY FACE BACK IN A BOOK. ANY WAY I CAN CONVINCE YOU TO KEEP IT THERE?

GOOD ONE, BEN...

NOW *WHERE* DID I KEEP MY *SUMO SLAMMER CARDS*...?

63

IT'S HERE!

IT'S HERO TIME!

FWOOOOSH

THAT REALLY *BURNS ME UP!* DO YOU KNOW HOW LONG IT TOOK ME TO BUILD THAT COLLECTION?

I ALW... DID HA... TEMP...

TIM... TO C... OF...

64

LET'S GO!

Put your brain cells to the test with this alien-tastic quiz. You'll need to turn back to other pages in the book to get some of the answers. Write your answers in the spaces. When you've got them all, take just the first letter of each word, and write them in the spaces at the bottom.

IF YOU GET THEM ALL CORRECT, YOU'LL SPELL THE NAME OF ONE OF BEN'S ALIEN DUDES!

1 In the story 'Lazy Day', which alien does Ben turn into?

that guy big chill

2 Turn to page 57. You need the 7-letter word from Alien X's grid.

reality

3 In the story 'Double Trouble', what is the name of the guy pretending to be Ben?

albedo

4 The Forever Knights trade in

_ _ _ _ _ _ _ _ _

alien technology.

66

5 Turn to page 43. You need the 4th word from the Cryptic Code.

not

6 What day of the week is it in the story 'Lazy Day'?

saterday

7 At the beginning of the story 'Ship Shape', what vehicle has Ship turned into?

a tank

8 In the story 'Double Trouble', we learn that Azmuth created the

o m n a t r i x

9 In the story 'The Past is the Key to the Future', what does Big Chill enter, to find the key?

sumoslamercardbox

10 The first name of Ben and Gwen's Grandpa.

max

/

ANSWERS

PAGE 7 FIND GRANDPA MAX!

The 10 hidden images of Grandpa Max are on pages 12, 14, 25, 27, 30, 40, 43, 44, 57 and 66.

PAGE 13 TANGLED ROOTS

Trail C leads to the bad guy.
The baddy is a DNAlien.

PAGE 15 LASER BLASTER

ChromaStone 3 will bring down the bad guy.

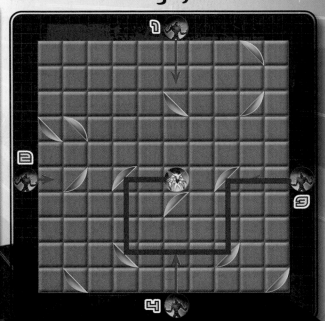

PAGE 27 SPEEDY MISSION A is the quickest route.

PAGE 29 ULTIMATE POWER

PAGE 31 WEB SEARCH

The hidden object is OMNITRIX.

PAGE 41 IDENTI-GOOP B and C are identical.

PAGE 43 CRYPTIC CODE
The message is: These creatures must not beat us.

PAGE 45 NOW YOU SEE HIM . . .

1 = E   2 = H    3 = C    4 = F

PAGE 55 ECHO DRAW

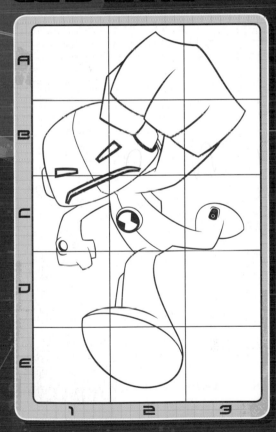

PAGE 57 ALIEN X'S GRID

PAGES 66 AND 67 LET'S GO!
1 – Big Chill, 2 – Reality, 3 – Albedo,
4 – Illegal, 5 – Not, 6 – Saturday, 7 – Tank,
8 – Omnitrix, 9 – Rust Bucket, 10 – Max.

Brain Storm is the hero alien dude.